Better Conversatic

A Guide for Relatives

The aim of this guide is to help people living with aphasia to have better conversations. It provides ideas, inspiration and examples all based on what people with aphasia and their families have developed working with the team at Connect.

The ideas series has been designed to make it accessible to people with aphasia.

Connect – the communication disability network
16-18 Marshalsea Road, London SE1 1HL
Telephone: 020 7367 0840
Email: info@ukconnect.org
www.ukconnect.org

connect
the communication disability network

Acknowledgements

This guide has been produced by Gwen Knight and the team at Connect. We would like to thank all of the people with aphasia, relatives and friends who have contributed their ideas and experiences. We would also like to thank the Aphasia Institute, Toronto for their inspiring work in the area of conversations.

© 2011 Connect - the communication disability network

Registered charity no.1081740

Illustrations © 2005 Caroline Firenza

First published 2005
Reprinted 2009, 2011

Printed and bound in Great Britain

ISBN 978-0-9536042-2-7

British Library Cataloguing in Publication Data
A catalogue record for this book is available from the British Library

Although every effort has been made to ensure that the content of this book is accurate, the authors and the publisher cannot be held responsible for any loss or claim arising out of the use of the suggestions made.

Contents

If you have any ideas and suggestions to improve this guide or for
another guide, please contact:

Connect – the communication disability network
16-18 Marshalsea Road, London SE1 1HL
Telephone: 020 7367 0840
Email: publications@ukconnect.org
www.ukconnect.org

About aphasia

Aphasia is a communication disability which occurs when the communication centres of the brain are damaged. It is usually caused by stroke, but can also be caused by head injury or tumours.

Each person with aphasia experiences it differently. Some people cannot speak at all, others can no longer read, write or use numbers. Everyday activities such as having a conversation, answering the phone, watching television, may suddenly become a source of profound frustration and anxiety both for the person with aphasia and for their families, friends and carers.

About Connect

Connect is a national charity working collaboratively with people with aphasia to provide practical, creative and lasting solutions. Connect promotes effective services, new opportunities and a better qualityof life for people living with aphasia (communication disability often caused by stroke). We aim to enable people living with aphasia to:

- Reconnect with life again
- Have a voice in the wider community
- Have access to a wide range of appropriate therapy and support

All proceeds from our publishing are used to support our work.

Introduction/How to use this guide

This **Connect** ideas guide explores the **issues** faced by family and friends in **communicating** with someone who has **aphasia**.

Relatives of people with aphasia have told us about the **difficulties** they encounter having conversations, and some of the ways they have found to **overcome** them.

We have gathered together a **wealth of ideas and suggestions** from relatives and, in this guide, will **share** them with you.

All the information here comes from the **personal experiences of relatives** and the **expertise** they have gained from years of **living with aphasia**.

1. What is conversation?

First of all, let's think about what conversation is.

Think of the many **different conversations** you might have during the course of a day.

Who do you have conversations with?

- ? Friends
- ? Family
- ? Work colleagues
- ? Shop assistants
- ? Neighbours
- ? Bank or Post Office clerks
- ? Someone else

Why do we have conversations?

- ? Get to know someone
- ? Gossip
- ? Have fun
- ? Share ideas
- ? Have a moan
- ? Argue and make up
- ? Find things out
- ? Get and give advice
- ? Pass the time
- ? Tell a story

- ? Console someone
- ? Something else
- ? Tease someone

Why are conversations so **important**?

Amongst other things, they enable us to:
- **Play a part** in life
- Build **connections** with others
- **Share** thoughts, feelings, ideas, concerns
- Make important **decisions**
- Express **who we are**

Conversations are important to us, and **just as important** to people with aphasia.

How do conversations **work**?

If we have no difficulty communicating we probably never think about how conversations work – we just **take them for granted**. But stop for a moment and think about what are the **components** of a **good conversation** – and a **not so good** conversation!

2011 © Connect - the communication disability network

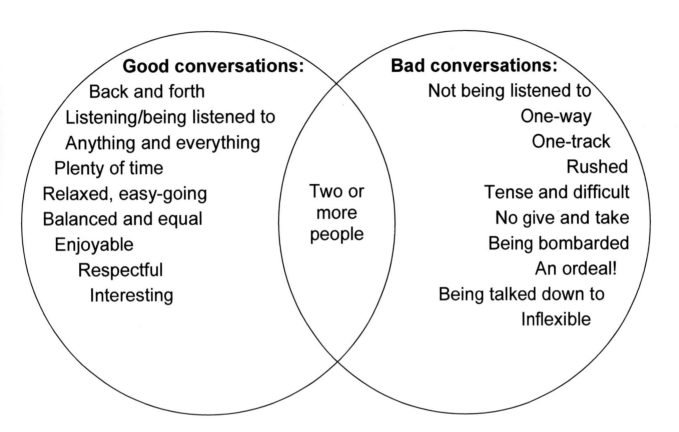

Good conversations:
Back and forth
Listening/being listened to
Anything and everything
Plenty of time
Relaxed, easy-going
Balanced and equal
Enjoyable
Respectful
Interesting

Two or more people

Bad conversations:
Not being listened to
One-way
One-track
Rushed
Tense and difficult
No give and take
Being bombarded
An ordeal!
Being talked down to
Inflexible

These components are just as **relevant – even more so** – when having a conversation with someone with **aphasia.**

Next, we will look at how aphasia affects conversation.

2.   How aphasia affects conversation

In this chapter, we are going to look at how **everyday conversations** are **affected by aphasia.**

Over the years, **relatives** have said to us:

- 🗣 It's **impossible** to have a **proper conversation** now
- 🗣 I **don't know how** to have a conversation with him
- 🗣 I don't know **where to start**
- 🗣 Our world has shrunk – it's **hard** to **find things to talk about** now
- 🗣 It takes **so long** to say a simple thing
- 🗣 He gets so **frustrated** when he can't say what he wants to say

- 🗣 I haven't got the **time** – there are **so many other things** to deal with
- 🗣 I'm too **tired**
- 🗣 She gets **angry** if I **can't understand** what she is saying
- 🗣 I don't know if I should **say the word** for him or **let him struggle.**
- 🗣 Whatever I do is wrong!
- 🗣 I don't have the **patience**

One thing is clear – it is **NOT easy**! It's **hard** having a conversation with someone with aphasia, especially when you are having to **cope** with so many **other things** too.

One reason that conversations are difficult may be that **life has changed** for you both. Let's think about the **topics** that might be discussed in a partnership and family **before stroke and aphasia**.

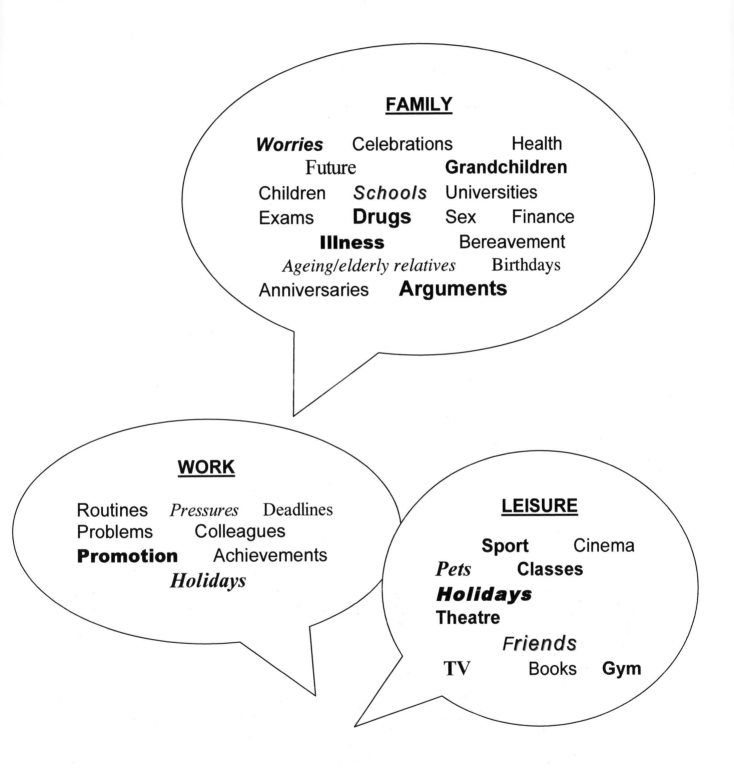

FINANCE

Salary   Savings   **Benefits**
Tax   *Insurance*
Housing   **Debts**   *Holidays*
School/university fees
Bank accounts

PAST
Shared Experiences
Work   **Travel**
Childhood
Memories

OTHER

The world around
Politics   **Gossip**
Local issues   News

DAY TO DAY TOPICS

Shopping **Housework**
Childcare
Appointments   Food
Clothing

Personal Relationships

Now let's look at what sort of topics arise in conversations relatives report having **after** stroke and aphasia, when life may have changed considerably:

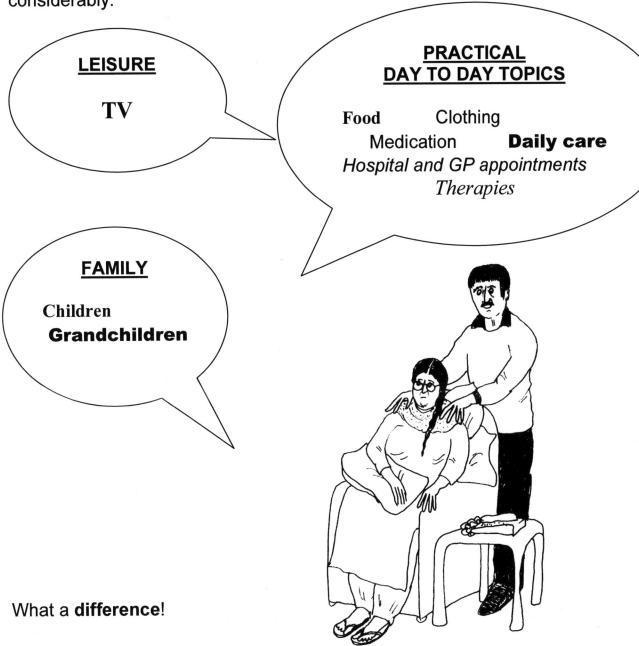

LEISURE

TV

PRACTICAL DAY TO DAY TOPICS

Food   Clothing
Medication   **Daily care**
Hospital and GP appointments
Therapies

FAMILY

Children
Grandchildren

What a **difference**!

What has happened to that **richness** of conversation?

Is it so surprising that **conversation** has **dwindled**, when life has **changed** so much?

How can you **re-gain** some of the **conversations** that you used to have?

If some topics of conversation have **dried up** because the **situation has changed**, could you:

? Talk about **new topics**

? Talk about **different aspects** of the closed down topic

? Talk about an old topic in **new ways**

Let's now turn to **how** conversations with someone with **aphasia** might be **different**.

This is what people living with aphasia have told us:

🗣 I **miss** the **spontaneity**

🗣 I have to **think before I speak**

🗣 It's **impossible** to **share a joke** now – he doesn't get it

🗣 He was the person I **shared everything** with – now I **can't**

🗣 Conversation is so **limited** now. I **miss** the **discussions** we used to have – we **can't even argue** anymore

🗣 I **wasn't prepared** for the **silence** of aphasia

So, what is difficult about having a conversation when you have **aphasia**? People with aphasia tell us:

🗣 Finding **words**

🗣 Everything takes much **longer**

🗣 People talk **too quickly**

🗣 Feeling under **pressure**

- 🗣 **Embarrassed**
- 🗣 Several people **talking at same time**
- 🗣 Keeping track
- 🗣 People **finishing** off **sentences**
- 🗣 People **butting in**
- 🗣 **Feeling anxious**
- 🗣 **Can't concentrate for long**
- 🗣 Getting **tired** very quickly
- 🗣 Background **noise**
- 🗣 People **don't give me time**
- 🗣 Can only do **one thing** at a time

It's important to stress that **no-one** can be expected to just know intuitively how to communicate with someone with aphasia.
Having a conversation with someone who has aphasia doesn't happen automatically, but it can be **made easier** with **support and techniques**.

In the following sections of this guide, we will share with you the **hints and tips** for making conversations easier, that other relatives have passed on.

3.   Making conversations easier

What might **help** to make **conversations easier**? What might **help** the person with aphasia **take in** what is being said and **express** what he or she wants to say? We asked the **experts, people with aphasia** and their **families**, for their ideas and **tips.**

People with aphasia say:

- 🗣 **Write** it down
- 🗣 **Don't talk so fast**
- 🗣 **Listen**
- 🗣 Give me **time**
- 🗣 Treat me as an **equal**
- 🗣 Be **clear** – one subject at a time
- 🗣 **One-to-one** is best
- 🗣 **Look** at me as you speak
- 🗣 **Don't make assumptions**

Relatives say:

- 🗣 Keep a sense of **humour!**
- 🗣 Take **pressure off** speech - encourage drawing and writing and gesture
- 🗣 Cut out **distractions** (for example switch off TV, radio, phone)
- 🗣 Use **writing, drawing, gesture yourself**
- 🗣 **Check** things **out**, especially **yes** and **no**
- 🗣 Accept sometimes conversation will get stuck – maybe **leave it and come back to it later**
- 🗣 Stay **calm** and **relaxed**

So, thinking back to why **conversations** are **important**, what can you do to help the person with aphasia to:

- **enjoy** a conversation
- take part on **equal terms**
- get a **point across** and **take in** what is being said
- play an **equal part** in **decision making**
- feel **involved**, valued, important
- **share** views, thoughts, feelings
- feel **engaged in** life

In summary, here are some things that you can do to help conversations go well:

- 👍 Pen and paper **to hand**
- 👍 Plenty of **time**
- 👍 Be **clear, one idea at a time**
- 👍 Write down **key words** as you go through the conversation

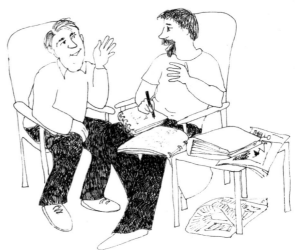

- 👍 Use **drawings**
- 👍 **Use drawing and writing yourself** and encourage the person with aphasia to use them too
- 👍 Use your key words and drawings to **check back** and **summarise**
- 👍 Use **gesture**
- 👍 Confirm **yes and no**
- 👍 Check that you and the person with aphasia have **both understood**
- 👍 Use **props** (photos, maps, calendars)

So many things to think of! So, where to **start**....?

Having a conversation with someone with aphasia means **both parties** have to **work harder** and be more **flexible** and **resourceful**. A few things to bear in mind:

- Some **techniques** work **better** for **some people** than others
- **Don't** attempt them **all at once**!
- Try **one or two techniques** and see how it goes
- Remember everyone has **good and bad days**, so try not to get discouraged
- **Tiredness** affects aphasia and makes it harder to find the words
- **Step** by **step**
- With each small step, give yourself a **pat on the back** – you are doing a great job!
- Remember, things **do change** over time.

Three years after her husband's stroke left him with **severe aphasia**, Julia was still **struggling** to have a **conversation** with him. Talking to members of a relatives' group she said:

🗣 "You know what the problem is – the **problem** is that we know this, what we should be doing – **but we're waiting for our husbands to speak**. But they're not going to speak – so we should **get on** with doing what we should be doing – **helping them to communicate**."

Since then, Julia has set aside **30 minutes** a day to have a **conversation** with David. She realised that conversations were one thing that had been **lost** and that she **missed**.

 She says that the **topics** often come from her, and that she is doing a lot of **writing down** to support conversation, but that her **husband** is now **contributing** by **writing down letters** and **drawing**. It's **not easy,** but Julia and David are beginning to have 'real' **conversations** again.

In the next section, we are going to look at some of the things which might **get in the way** of having a **conversation** with someone with aphasia and explore some ways of **getting round** them.

4. Barriers to conversation – finding your way through

So what things **get in the way** of having a **conversation** with someone with **aphasia**?

Some of the more **obvious barriers** for you may be:

- **Not knowing** what to do
- Not having enough **time**
- Being too **tired**
- Being too **busy**
- **Frustration**

But are there other things which make **conversations difficult**? When we have explored this a little more deeply with relatives, a number of **less tangible**, but equally **important**, **barriers** have surfaced:

- ☞ **Embarrassment**
- ☞ **Fear of getting it wrong**
- ☞ Feeling **overwhelmed**
- ☞ **Impatience** – having to repeat over and over
- ☞ **Pain** of watching your partner **struggle**
- ☞ Own **emotional** turmoil
- ☞ Fear of partner becoming **upset** or **angry**
- ☞ Conversation feeling **unnatural**

You may recognise some of these barriers. But everyone is **different.** So what are the **solutions**?

In the earlier sections of this guide there are a few practical **suggestions** that might help if you simply **don't know** what to do.

Some of the **other barriers** are less easy to deal with, as they are more **emotional** than practical.

Sometimes it is enough to **know** that these barriers **do exist**, they **are important** and **other people do experience** them too. You are **not alone**.

It **is hard** to see your **partner struggle**. There **will be times** when you both get **upset and angry**. It **is understandable** to get **impatient** and feel like giving up. There **will be times** when you are too **tired** or too **busy** to persevere with a conversation that seems to be going nowhere.

Initially, it **may feel unnatural** to use drawing, writing, and gesture in your conversations. But hopefully, as time goes on, with both of you communicating in this way, it will **begin to feel more natural**.

If you find yourself facing some of the barriers listed above:

- 👍 Give yourself a **break**
- 👍 **Don't** be **too hard** on yourself
- 👍 **Accept** that sometimes things will get in the way
- 👍 **Congratulate** yourself on the conversations that **do go well,** and build on them
- 👍 **Try not to dwell** on the conversations that don't go well.

 2011 © Connect - the communication disability network

5. Difficult topics

It can be **hard enough** having a **conversation** with someone with aphasia when talking about **everyday things**.

But what about more **tricky subjects** that can be hard to discuss even if there are no communication difficulties? Such as:

- **Personal relationships and problems**
- **Sex**
- **Financial** problems and decisions
- **Care** decisions
- Changes in **lifestyle**
- Planning for the **future**
- **Grief and loss**

How do you go about **tackling** these topics? You might feel it's an **impossible** task and therefore **avoid** them - an **understandable** reaction.

But they **are important**.

They are probably decisions and discussions you **shared** with your partner **before stroke and aphasia** got in the way.

It is worth **having a go** at discussing these topics – to feel that you are **both involved** in making important decisions and **sharing** the **responsibility**.

There are a number of things that can help. First of all, it's important to create the **right conditions for your conversation**. Choose a time when you and your partner are:

- 👍 **Not tired**
- 👍 **Not stressed**
- 👍 **Not angry**
- 👍 **Not under pressure**
- 👍 **Not pushed for time**
- 👍 **Not likely to be interrupted**

These are things you would probably have taken into consideration before aphasia. They are **no different** now!

Now let's think about what **is different**. Building on the **tips** we have given earlier in the guide, is there anything else that would **help**?

Here are some **ideas** which we have picked up from relatives:

- 👍 Do some **preparation in advance**
- 👍 **Think through** the **points** you want to discuss
- 👍 Tell your partner you want this to be a **joint decision**
- 👍 It might help to **prepare** some **key words** or **bullet points**
- 👍 **You may want to try drawing or making diagrams** to convey some of the main ideas

- 👍 Have **options** to choose from - again having these clearly written down can help the person with aphasia to choose and decide with you

- 👍 Take plenty of **time**

- 👍 It may be appropriate to have **someone there to support** you both (for example your GP, Social Worker, Speech & Language Therapist, Counsellor)

- 👍 And, of course, don't forget your **props** – calendar, maps, pictures and photos

- 👍 With these more sensitive topics, it really helps to try and **summarise** what you have discussed and decided

- 👍 **Check out** with the person who has aphasia that he or she **understands and agrees** with your summary. You are both agreed

It may involve some **thought and forward planning** but think how **rewarding** it will be for both of you to know that you have arrived at a **decision together**. An **equal partnership!**

6. When things go wrong

You are now a **skilled** conversation partner – **Congratulations!**

But, realistically, there will still be **times** when things **go wrong**, when the conversation gets **stuck**, when you just **can't work out** what your partner is trying to tell you.

What do you do then?

Here are some words of **advice** from **people living with aphasia** about what to do when conversation breaks down:

- 👍 Stay **relaxed**
- 👍 Give **time**
- 👍 **Accept** that it **will** happen
- 👍 **Don't pretend** that you understand if you don't
- 👍 **Acknowledge** the breakdown- and that you both share the responsibility for it. It is no-one's fault

- 👍 **Check** if it's really **important** or **urgent**
- 👍 Give the option of **coming back** to the topic later
- 👍 Agree **when** to **come back** to it
- 👍 Keep a **note** of it so you remember what you are coming back to!
- 👍 Be **sensitive** and responsive to your partner
- 👍 Above all, **don't be discouraged.**

7.   Helping other people to have conversations

Before the stroke in your family, had you **heard** of **aphasia**? **Probably not**. You've had **no choice** but to **learn** about it very quickly.

But **most people** your partner comes into contact with will still be in blissful **ignorance**! They will **know nothing at all** about **aphasia** and will have **no idea** how to even **begin** to **communicate**. This is where you come in: **you** can make an **enormous difference**, with your knowledge and expertise, in **helping other people** to have a conversation with the person with aphasia.

Your relative is probably in daily contact with lots of different people:

Other family members
Friends   *Neighbours*
Shopkeepers   **Bus drivers**
GP   *Day Centre staff and members*
Therapy group   **Hospital staff**

People try their best but sometimes **do things** – albeit unwittingly – which the person with aphasia **does not find helpful**, such as:

- Making the person **repeat** words over and over
- **Interrupting**
- **Finishing sentences**
- Talking very **loudly**
- Trying to **teach the person to speak**
- **Telling** them what they need to do.

Some people are so **completely at a loss**, they don't **know** where to **start**. So maybe they might:

- **Ignore** the person with aphasia
- **Talk over** them
- Direct a question to **you** rather than to the person with aphasia
- Talk **about** the person with aphasia rather than **to** him
- **Exclude** the person from a conversation in a group.

It is understandable that other people might feel **nervous** and **embarrassed**. So, what can **you** do to **help them** feel more **comfortable** and **confident** about having a **conversation** that everyone **enjoys**?

Remember, **showing** people how to communicate is always much more effective than **telling** them.

By being **relaxed**, talking **naturally**, **involving** the person with aphasia, using your communication **props** and keeping your **sense of humour** you can **model** how to have a **good conversation**.

If someone asks you a question **about** your partner (for example 'Is he going to a day centre?') re-direct it **to** your partner instead.

Pass on tips and techniques that you have found useful.

🗣 George said: 'My wife and I have made up our own hand gestures for certain things. We are continually adding to them.
I make sure our family and friends know about them so they can use them too'.

Does your partner use a **communication book** (a book containing words and pictures of everyday things, and important people and places that he or she can point to)?

👍 Demonstrate how to use it with the person with aphasia.

In more **formal** situations, such as visit to the **GP**, here are some tips relatives have suggested to ensure that the person with aphasia is **included** in the discussion:

👍 Ask for **extra time** (perhaps book a double appointment)

👍 **Prepare** questions in advance

👍 Maybe write a **checklist** to take with you

👍 Make sure you have **pen and paper**

👍 Again, **show** good techniques, by writing down **key words**, directing questions to your partner and so on

👍 **Ask** the **other person** in the conversation to do the **same**

Sometimes, relatives tell us, friends stop visiting because they **don't know what to talk about** or how to **keep a conversation going**.

Here are some **ideas** from relatives and people with aphasia:

👍 Keep family and friends **up-dated** on what is happening in your lives so they have a **starting point** for conversation

👍 Make a personal **portfolio** or **life book** with the person who has aphasia. This is a book or folder that **represents** in words, pictures, letters and documents the **person's life**. It could cover family, friends, interests, hobbies, work, places visited, holidays: whatever the **person** wants to **include**. This is a great **source of conversation** for someone who may not know the person with aphasia very well

👍 **Newspapers** bring a little of the outside world to the person with aphasia and there is always something new to talk about. Pick an **interesting article** and read it out to the person with aphasia if they are not able to read it themselves. You could write down or draw the key points to discuss

👍 Watch a **TV programme**

together and share your

thoughts on it

👍 If the visitor knows the person with aphasia has a **particular interest** in something, the sky's the limit!

Look at this diagram to see how one topic can be explored in depth and lead to many others:

Divergent thinking

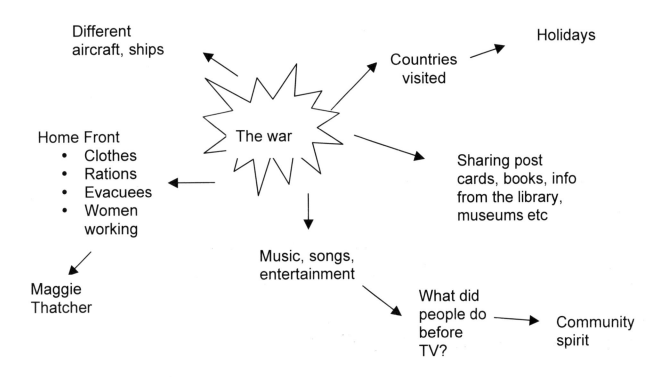

Here are some other **props** that relatives have found useful when **getting conversations going**, and **keeping them going**:

- 👍 TV Guide
- 👍 Radio Times
- 👍 Maps
- 👍 Postcards
- 👍 Photos
- 👍 Travel books / brochures
- 👍 Hello or OK magazines (great for all the latest gossip on celebrities!)
- 👍 Specific magazines on things that interest the person with aphasia, such as gardening, football, music, cars.
- 👍 If you have access to the Internet, looking at different websites together can open up many conversations. For example, if the person has an interest in local history, or family trees, searching for and surfing different sites together will give you lots to talk about

What a wealth of ideas! There's no excuse now for anyone to run out of things to talk about!

Impress on your friends: the most important thing is that the conversation should be **enjoyable and fun**, sharing common interests, relaxed and equal – definitely **NOT** a **teaching** session.

You can also help other people by letting them know what to expect.

For instance, people with aphasia often:

- tire very easily
- lose interest
- lose concentration
- might get upset
- might get frustrated

Reassure them that this is to be expected. They should try not to be put off by it or take it personally, but to keep relaxed.

Hopefully, this will help people to feel more **confident** and willing to pick up the conversation at another time.

- As one young son said: 'Some people are nervous of attempting to speak to people with aphasia, but they just have to give it a shot. Don't leave people with aphasia out of the conversation.'

8. Relatives and Conversations: Frequently Asked Questions

Over the years, we have found some **questions** come up time and time again. We asked a panel of **experts**, i.e. **people with aphasia**, how they would answer these questions. Here are their words of **advice**:

? **Should I finish off sentences for the person with aphasia?**

👍 A lot of people with aphasia find this **very annoying**. It rushes you and **doesn't give you time** to think. But for some people a **helpful suggestion is OK**, particularly when words are very hard to find.

? Does it help to **repeat words**?

👍 Sometimes **helpful as a way to practise words....**but not all the time. **Definitely** not helpful **in** everyday conversations.

? Does **drawing** help?

👍 Yes – when words go missing, it gives a **clue**

👍 It can take the **pressure off speech** and help the words to come

👍 Sometimes, **arrows and diagrams** are useful to help understanding and make connections between people and things

👍 It's a written record – words just evaporate in the air!

? Why do people have good days and bad days?

👍 It's very **common** – sometimes when you're **tired**, sometimes **not well**, sometimes **no reason**! Best to **take it easy** on bad days and come back to the conversation on a good day!

? What will help the speech get better in conversations?

👍 **Anything and everything**

👍 Whatever works for you

👍 **Doing more** things

👍 Being **involved**

👍 Getting your **confidence** back

👍 **Speech therapy**

👍 Having **good conversation partners**

? Why do people with aphasia come across as very blunt and direct?

👍 Aphasia **takes away the niceties** of language

👍 You have to **focus on what you are saying** – so sometimes you forget to do the nice social speech, e.g. 'How are you?'

👍 You need to **get the words out quickly** – while they are at the front of your brain

👍 **Not trying to be rude** – just aphasia!

9. Conclusion

In this Connect guide, we have looked at how aphasia affects conversations and have offered some **practical solutions** to some of the difficulties you may be facing.

What you do and **how you talk** with the person with aphasia can make a **huge difference** – both to your own conversations and to conversations between the person with aphasia and other people.

The ideas in this guide have been drawn from the **experiences of relatives and people with aphasia** – they've been tried out and they **do** help.

Remember, lots of people have faced the same difficulties that you are encountering – you are not alone.

🗣 As one relative said: 'It's a **learning process** for both of us. Things don't change overnight but small things **do** make a difference'.

Hopefully soon, if not already, you will begin to find conversations becoming more **enjoyable** and **equal** for everyone.

You should take credit and be proud of yourself. You are doing a
fantastic job!

Some useful references and contacts

<u>**Organisations**</u> <u>working with people with stroke and aphasia in the UK</u>

Connect - the communication disability network
16-18 Marshalsea Road, London SE1 1HL
Telephone: 020 7367 0840
Fax: 020 7367 0841
www.ukconnect.org

Different Strokes
9 Canon Harnett Court, Wolverton Mill,
Milton Keynes, MK12 5NF
Telephone: 0845 130 7172
www.differentstrokes.co.uk

Speakability
1 Royal Street, London SE1 7LL
Telephone: 020 7261 9572
Fax: 020 7928 9542
www.speakability.org.uk

The Stroke Association
240 City Road, London EC1V 2PR
Telephone: 020 7566 0330
Helpline: 0845 303 3100
Fax: 020 7490 2686
www.stroke.org.uk

Chest, Heart & Stroke Association Scotland (CHSS)
65 North Castle Street
Edinburgh, EH2 3LT
Telephone: 0845 077 6000
www.chss.org.uk

The Princess Royal Trust for Carers
Telephone: 020 7480 7788
www.carers.org

Carers National Association
Telephone: 020 7490 8818
www.carersonline.org.uk

Other useful websites

www.aphasiahelp.org – an accessible website about aphasia

www.aphasia.ca – website of the Aphasia Institute, Toronto

Other books about aphasia from Connect

The Stroke and Aphasia Handbook
Parr, S., Pound, C., Byng S., Moss, B, & Long, B. (2004)
Available from Connect - Tel. 020 7367 0840

The Connect Ideas Series
Caring and Coping
Having a Stroke Being a Parent
How to Volunteer
Available from Connect - Tel. 020 7367 0840

Other useful books

Talking about Aphasia: Living with loss of language after stroke
Parr, S., Byng S., Gilpin, S., Ireland, C. (1997)
Open University Press

Aphasia Inside Out
Parr,S, Duchan, J and Pound,C (2003)
Open University Press

The man who lost his language
Hale, S (2002)
Penguin Books

Stroke at your fingertips
Rudd, A., Irwin, P., Penhale, B. (2000)
Class Publishing Ltd

The Selfish Pig's Guide to Caring
Hugh Marriott (2003)
Polperro Heritage Press

Your ideas and tips for better conversations: